CLOSE READING

Passages and Graphic Organizers for Everyday Practice

Grade 3

EP2561 © 2015 Demco, Inc.• 4810 Forest Run Road • Madison, WI 53704

www.edupress.com

ISBN 13: 978-1-56472-370-3

What Is Close Reading?

Close reading is thoughtful, critical analysis of a text. When using the strategy, students focus on significant details or patterns in order to develop a deep, precise understanding of the text. The reader directs his or her attention to the text itself instead of relying on background knowledge for comprehension and rereads a text multiple times to look closely at its meaning. This strategy is meant to level the playing field for students; if everyone has to answer questions using only information from what they read, all should be able to do so equally well. Those who have a wealth of background information have less of an advantage over those who don't. Close reading includes the following:

- Using short passages and excerpts
- Diving right into the text with limited pre-reading activities
- Focusing on the text itself instead of making connections to or relying on prior knowledge
- Rereading deliberately
- Reading with a pencil to mark and make notes during reading, including thoughts on interesting or exciting parts, questions, or other ideas
- Noticing things that are confusing and using fix-up strategies to make sense of the text (such as rereading or studying pictures or other text features)
- Discussing the text with others
- Using Think-Pair-Share or Turn-and-Talk frequently
- Working in small groups and as a class
- Responding to text-dependent questions

Steps in a Close Reading Lesson

Have your students reread your chosen text several times over several days and use the question stems on page 3 and the graphic organizers on pages 4 through 22 to help students focus their thoughts.

The following steps are meant to guide you in crafting a lesson that scaffolds students and focuses on increasingly complex text-dependent questions.

1. FIRST READ: Key Ideas and Details

Here you will focus on the most important elements of the text—key ideas and details. Set the purpose for reading, and have students read text as independently as possible. The first read should be done without building background knowledge; students should be making meaning from the text as they read. Focus on the big ideas in the text, making sure that readers know the main idea, story elements, and supporting details. They may use graphic organizers to shape their thinking.

Following the first read, pose a text-dependent question (see question stems on page 3), reminding students to find evidence from the text to support their answers. Then, have students Think-Pair-Share to assess what they have gleaned from the text. By listening as they share, you can determine how well the students understand the big ideas of the text, helping you focus future close readings.

2. SECOND READ: Craft and Structure

Here you will focus on how the text works. Use a text-dependent question to focus and set a purpose for rereading. For the second close read, have students reread a section that includes complex elements or ideas that they should explore to arrive at a deeper understanding of the text.

After rereading, students should discuss the text with partners or in small groups, focusing on the author's craft and organizational patterns. This may include vocabulary choices, text structure, or text features that the author included. Students use graphic organizers to record their ideas. After students share with partners or in small groups, have groups share with the entire class to assess understanding.

3. THIRD READ: Integration of Knowledge and Ideas

Here you will focus on what the text means to the reader and how it connects to other experiences. This reading of a text should go even deeper, requiring students to synthesize and analyze information from several texts or media. This is the perfect opportunity for students to relate the text they are reading to a theme or another text on a similar topic. They may record their ideas on sticky notes or graphic organizers. Have students journal a response to a text-dependent question. Focus the whole-class discussion on finding text evidence to support their ideas.

Text-Based Question Stems

Fiction

- What kind of text is this? (e.g., poem, drama, prose, etc.) How do you know?
- What big ideas should the reader take away after reading this?
- Which words really call our attention here? What do we notice as we reread them?
- What does [word or phrase from the story, figurative language, sensory word] mean?
- From whose point of view is this story told? Through whose eyes did you see this story?
- Describe how [name of character] responds to [major event or challenge].
- How does [character] show [character trait] in [title of text]?
- What do readers learn about the family's [or other characters'] relationship from this section?
- Based on the story, what can we infer about [two or more characters]?

- What was the [problem, solution, action, setting]?
- Describe the story structure, including beginning, middle, and ending.
- Explain cause-and-effect relationships in the story/text.
- What could the main character have learned that you could also learn?
- Analyze how [character] and [character] interact in this story.
- Explain how [character] changed in the story.
- What was a moral or lesson in the story?
- How does your own point of view compare to the narrator's on [topic]?
- Compare the text to a movie, web page, video game, piece of art or music, or other media.

Nonfiction

- What are the central ideas in this text?
- What have you learned from [title of text]?
- Look back at the text and see if you can divide it into parts. What parts does the author include?
- Summarize the key supporting details and ideas.
- Explain the meaning of [general academic vocabulary word].
- Explain what [domain/content specific word— e.g., isthmus] means.
- How do the author's choice of words and the tone of the language illuminate the author's point of view on the topic?
- How do the [pictures, charts, diagrams, photographs] help convey the mood of the story?
- What text features (e.g., headings, table of contents, glossary, electronic menu, icons) did the author include to help the reader?

- How did the author organize the ideas in the [article, book, etc.]?
- Explain the connections between a reason the author gave and the evidence he or she cited.
- What text structure did the author use in this text?
- Explain how you know that the author used [a text structure].
- Explain cause-and-effect relationships in the text.
- Explain similarities and differences between two texts on the same topic.
- Read [two or more accounts of the same event/ topic]. Analyze the information the authors present.
- How does this selection connect to [other text we have read, content area, the theme we are studying]?
- How does your own point of view compare to the author's on [topic]?

Story Elements

Characters

Setting

Title

Problem

Solution

Name _____

Be a Word Sleuth!

Word I don't know	The text says	So I think the word means

Word I don't know	The text says	So I think the word means

Word I don't know	The text says	So I think the word means

Word I don't know	The text says	So I think the word means

What's the Problem?

What is the problem faced by the character?

Why does the problem occur?

List three important events relating to the problem.

1 _____

2 _____

3 _____

How is the problem resolved?

Name _____

Making Inferences

Clues in the passage:

What I already know:

My Inference

Clues in the passage:

What I already know:

My Inference

Name _____

Nonfiction Text Features

Write two examples of text features found in the passage: bullets, graph, caption, illustration, map, subhead, sidebar, etc. Then describe how each helped you better understand the passage.

Text Feature

▶ _____
_____
_____
_____
_____
_____
_____

Text Feature

▶ _____
_____
_____
_____
_____
_____
_____

Name

Summarizing Nonfiction

List words that help you understand the passage.

What is the main idea of the passage?

What are four details that support the main idea of the passage?

FIGURATIVE LANGUAGE

Write an example of figurative language in the first box, then draw a picture of it. Finally, write what the author really means.

Example 1

_____
_____
_____
_____

➡️

_____
_____

Example 2

_____
_____
_____
_____

➡️

_____
_____

Picture Sequencing

In the boxes below, draw pictures of important events in the story, in the order they took place.

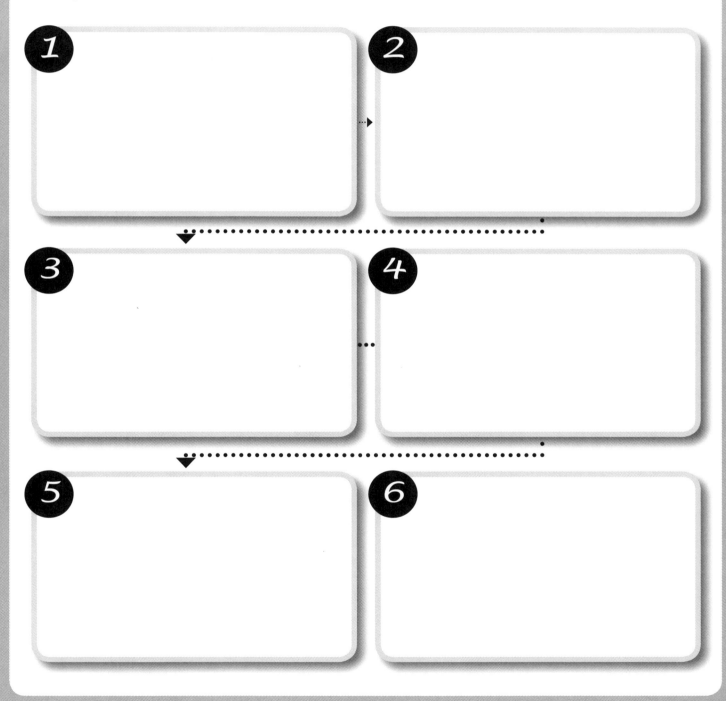

Main Idea and Details

Name

Write the main idea of the story in the tree. Then, write details that support the main idea in the apples.

Main Idea

Lesson Learned

Name _____

In the box below, draw a picture of the lesson that the main character learned in the story. Then, describe the lesson in your own words.

_____

_____

_____

_____

_____

_____

MAKING PREDICTIONS

Prediction	Change in Prediction	What Actually Happened

Visualizing the Story

In the spaces below, write what you experienced with your senses while reading the story. Then, draw a scene from the story that you visualized in your mind.

I see …	I hear …	I taste …

My Visualization

I feel …	I smell …

 # Drawing What You Learned

Use the information from the text to illustrate four facts you learned.

Fact: _____

_____

Fact: _____

_____

Fact: _____

_____

Fact: _____

_____

THE MAIN CHARACTER

What is your favorite thing about this character?

Draw a picture of the main character:

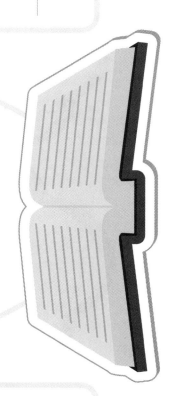

Describe the main character using adjectives:

1
2
3
4
5

Think About It

Think about what you learned while reading the passage. Fill in the spaces below.

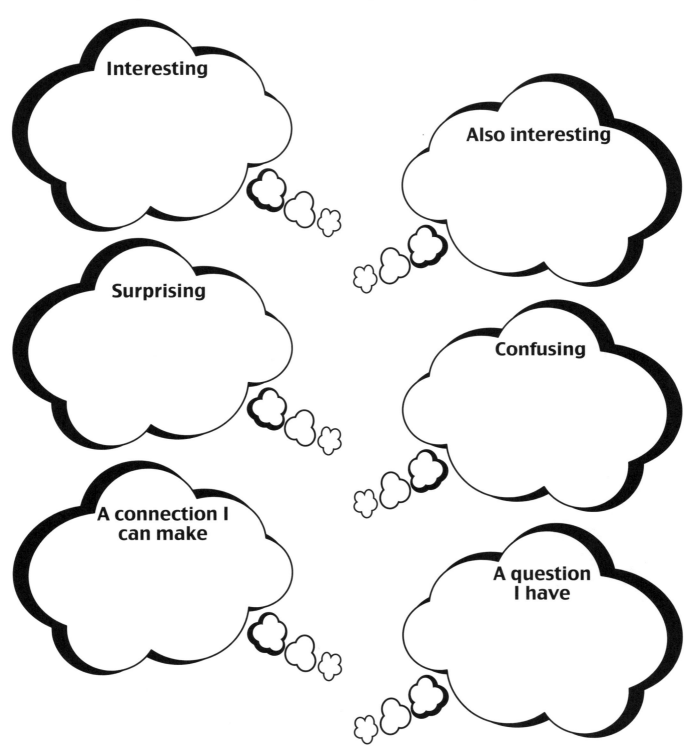

Interesting

Also interesting

Surprising

Confusing

A connection I can make

A question I have

Summarizing Fiction

Name _____

Write a one-sentence summary of the story.
Draw a detailed picture to match the summary.

_____

_____

_____

_____

Name _____

Cause and Effect

Directions: Identify the causes and effects of events in the story.

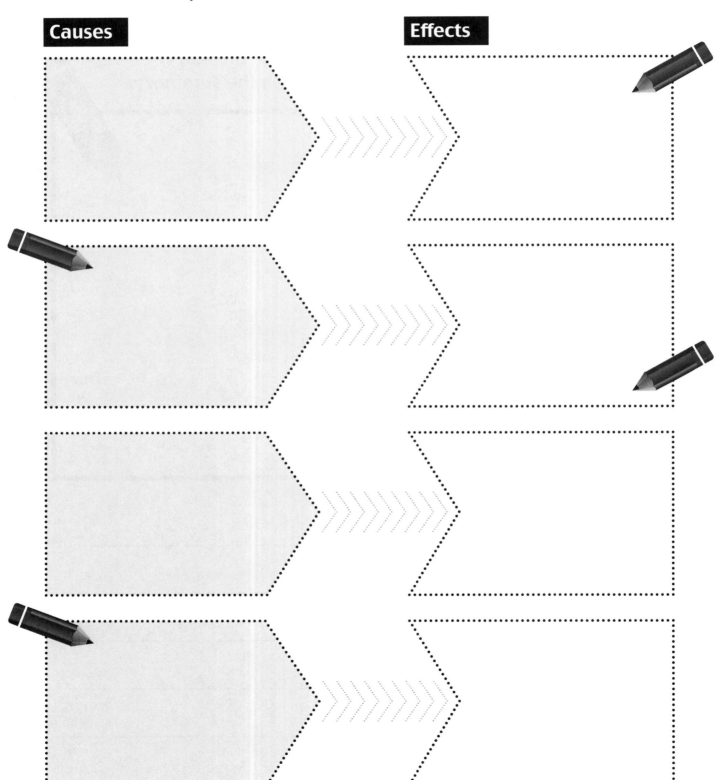

Causes

Effects

Name _____

ANALYZING CHARACTER TRAITS

Read the passage. Choose three traits that describe the main character. Write evidence from the text to support your choices.

Character's Name

Trait 1	Evidence

Trait 2	Evidence

Trait 3	Evidence

What's the Author's Purpose?

The author's purpose is

_____

_____

_____

_____

_____

I know this because

_____

_____

_____

_____

_____

Draw a picture that shows evidence of the author's purpose.

A breeze blows across the meadow. The tall grasses bow to its power. Alice plants her boot on the bottom rung of the fence, grabs hold of the top rung, and hoists herself up. She whistles a few bars of Windy's favorite song, and her pony gallops to the fence. Alice leans over the fence and feeds the pony a carrot. Then she pats her neck.

Windy whinnies as Dad walks toward the fence. Then the pony gallops off onto the field. Dad says, "We need to get her used to the barn. I think you're the only one she will follow. We'll start barn training her tomorrow. Are you up to the task?"

Alice hops down from the fence. She knows her new pony likes the freedom of the open shelter in the field. With only three walls, the shelter allows Windy to trot into the field whenever she wants to do so. She also knows that teaching a pony to go into a barn can be as difficult as teaching a dog to stop barking. "Why does Windy have to get used to the barn so soon? She likes staying in the field shelter."

"She can still stay in the shelter, but we get some bad storms out here. Sometimes the barn is the safest place for our horses."

The next morning, Alice watches Windy zigzag across the field. Alice walks into the field and whistles. Windy walks slowly toward her. She sniffs at the apple in Alice's hand before eating it. "Good girl," Alice whispers.

Alice walks alongside Windy as she pats her back and speaks softly. They are about 10 feet from the gate when Windy snorts and rears, waving her front hooves in the air. Then Windy turns and gallops out into the field. Dad joins Alice.

Alice looks at Windy, who is nibbling on some grass at the far end of the field. "This is going to be harder than I thought it would be," Alice says.

Dad rests his hand on Alice's shoulder. "You got her to walk with you today," he says. "If you make a little progress like that every day, before long you'll have Windy going to the barn happily."

Every morning, Alice tries again. Finally, Windy makes it all the way to the gate. The next day, Dad stands by the gate. Alice and Windy walk toward him. When they get close, he opens the gate. Windy snorts and stops. Alice soothes Windy with her soft voice. "You can do it, Windy, I know you can." Windy takes a few more steps toward the open barn doors. Alice praises Windy. "You're doing great," she says. Windy walks into the barn and looks around. Alice feeds a peppermint to her pony and rubs her back. "You did it!" Alice says.

The Boy Who Cried Wolf

Long ago, there was a mischievous boy who lived on a steep hill with his parents. One day, his father was preparing to leave on a long trip. "You must be responsible for our sheep while I am gone," he said to the boy. "Guard them like diamonds and keep them safe."

Every morning, the boy's mother woke him at sunrise. Then she packed the boy a lunch and sent him out to the meadow.

The boy did not like his new job one bit. The sheep munched on grass all day. They didn't want to play games with the boy. The boy sat under a tree and spied on the people hurrying about in the village. Then he waited to hear his mother ring the dinner bell so he could bring the four-legged cotton balls back to the farm.

This continued day after day. One afternoon, he was sitting under the tree, watching the people in the village below. The boy watched as the villagers carried bundles from place to place. They stopped to greet their neighbors along the way, talking and laughing. The boy didn't think it was fair that the villagers were acting like they were at a party while he stayed in the meadow alone with his sheep. Then he got an idea. He smiled, stood up, and ran down the hill into the village. "Help, help, a wolf is chasing my sheep!" he shouted.

The villagers dropped what they were doing and ran up the steep hill to help him. When they reached the sheep, they saw there was no wolf. The boy laughed. He liked playing tricks on people.

A few days later, the boy ran into the village again. "Help, help, a wolf is chasing my sheep!" he shouted. Once again, the villagers raced up the hill, and once again, there was no wolf. The boy looked at the red faces of the villagers. He held his sides and rolled on the ground laughing. *These people are so easy to trick!* he thought.

The next week, the boy sat under the tree watching his sheep. Suddenly, a wolf sprang out from behind the tree and began chasing the sheep. The frightened boy ran down into the village. "Help, help, a wolf is chasing my sheep!" he shouted.

The villagers shook their heads and walked away. One woman stopped and said, "You've tricked us twice, but you won't trick us again."

The boy raced back up the hill. The wolf had already chased all the sheep away. The boy went home to his mother and confessed what he had done. His mother shook her head. "I hope this teaches you an important lesson."

A beautiful ribbon dangles from Aunt Lucy's hand. It is purple and gray with a gold thread running through it. "That ribbon will look lovely in my hair," Vivi says.

"If it looks wonderful in your hair, it will look wonderful in my hair too," says Vivi's sister, Sophie.

"You both can share the ribbon," Aunt Lucy promises.

"Who gets to wear it first?" Vivi asks.

Aunt Lucy laughs. "I'll hide the ribbon. After lunch, whoever finds the ribbon gets to wear it first."

Aunt Lucy slides a pan in the oven and glances out the window. "While you girls prepare a salad, I'll set the table outside. A robin is building a nest in the tree by the patio. It is officially spring. That means eating outside."

Once the table is set, Aunt Lucy steps back to look at it. The pail in the center of the table will hold lilacs later in the season. For now, it holds extra napkins. Aunt Lucy tucks the ribbon inside the pail with the napkins. Then she pulls up a small loop so the ribbon peeks over the pail's rim.

During lunch, Sophie asks, "Will you give us a hint about the ribbon?"

"One of you will discover it on your own," Aunt Lucy answers.

After lunch, the girls hunt around the yard. Vivi notices Aunt Lucy clearing the table. "We'll help you clean up, and then we'll find the ribbon," Vivi says, as she picks up the pail of napkins.

"Leave the pail on the table!" Aunt Lucy says. Vivi returns the pail, removes the napkins, and returns them to the kitchen. A few minutes later, Aunt Lucy peers into the pail. "Who has the ribbon?" Aunt Lucy frowns. "I hid it in the pail."

Vivi and Sophie look at each other. "Did you find it?" they say, sounding like a chorus.

Vivi hurries in and out of the kitchen. "The ribbon isn't with the extra napkins," she says.

Sophie searches the patio under the table. "There's nothing shiny or silky down here," she says.

The robin, with a piece of grass in its beak, swoops over their heads. "Robin, I wish you could speak to us. I bet you see everything from your nest. You could tell us what happened to the ribbon," Aunt Lucy says.

Vivi looks up at the bird's nest and laughs. The sunlight bounces off flecks of gold in the nest. "The robin is the ribbon thief! It wove it into its nest."

"I'm sorry, girls, now neither of you gets to wear the ribbon."

Sophie answers, "True, but the robin needs it more than we do!"

The boys gather around the coach. "We didn't lose our last game because the opposing team has better skills than we have. The other team won because they are better at teamwork," Coach says. "Today we're going to work on that. The park is changing the location of the refreshment stand. You are going to move all the food cartons from the old building behind us to the new building up on the hill."

"That's just grunt work," Jay says. "How will that improve our teamwork?"

Coach explains, "Tommy twisted his knee and can't run up and down the hill today. You boys have to come up with a plan that includes every member of the team. Live up to our team name, the Eagles, and you will soar at this task."

After Coach walks away, Jay says, "The solution is simple. Tommy can walk up and down the hill, while the rest of us run."

Tommy says, "That's not going to work. Walking on a hill feels like a construction worker has taken a jackhammer to my knee."

"Ouch!" Malcolm says. "Hmmm. Does it hurt to stand? Can you lift boxes without damaging your knee?"

"I can stand and walk on flat ground without pain," Tommy says, flexing his arms. "And I'm still as strong as Hercules."

"Last week, I read a biography of Henry Ford," Jay says. "We can use his invention to solve our problem."

The boys all laugh. Malcolm says, "That would make sense if any of us were old enough to drive, which we aren't."

"It makes sense because Ford's greatest invention was the assembly line," Jay explains. "It helped his company make cars faster and cheaper. We could make our own assembly line."

"That sounds like a good idea," says Tommy. "That way, I can do my fair share of the work."

The boys line up side by side. Tommy stands on the flat ground by the old building. Malcolm takes the spot at the top of the hill by the new building. "Ready?" Jay shouts.

"Ready!" the boys answer.

Tommy lifts the first carton and passes it to Jay. The box travels from boy to boy up the human chain. When Malcolm puts the carton in the new building, he shouts, "Our assembly line is a success! Now let's pick up the pace!"

In less than an hour, the last carton is traveling up the hill. When it reaches its new home, Coach gathers the team together. "Excellent job, guys! What did we learn from this?"

Jay says, "Every job is easier when you work like a team."

The tiny blacksmith shop was dim. Barely a glint of sunlight made it inside. Still, the room was hotter than a wood stove. Josiah knew he was lucky to be an apprentice to the village blacksmith. His friend Abe was training with the village rope maker, and his hands bled every night from handling the rough fibers.

But Josiah wished Mr. Cooper would let him do more than make nails. He had been training with the blacksmith for almost a year. Every time Josiah asked for a chance to learn something new, Mr. Cooper would answer, "A good apprentice learns from every task, even those he has done many times. Making nails helps you become an expert at handling a hammer and tongs. It can teach you to be careful around the hot metal. These are lessons that will serve you well if you have a shop of your own someday."

One day, the blacksmith shop was hot enough to boil water. Josiah was hard at work hammering out nails. Mr. Cooper was working at the big anvil. He was making a new meat fork for Mrs. Williams. Josiah paused to wipe the sweat from his brow and watch Mr. Cooper at work. He hoped someday he would swing a hammer as well as Mr. Cooper did.

Josiah got back to work. The next time he looked up, he saw Mr. Cooper's spectacles sliding down his sweaty nose. In an instant, the glasses fell from his face and onto the anvil. Mr. Cooper tried to stop the heavy hammer in his hand, but it was too late. The iron hammer landed on the spectacles. They broke into many little pieces.

Mr. Cooper moaned. "Mrs. Williams is one of my best customers. I promised she would have her meat fork by tomorrow. I can't do my best work without my spectacles." He looked distraught.

Josiah said, "Please let me help. I will be your eyes and your hands. Tell me what to do, and I will follow your directions."

Mr. Cooper gave Josiah directions one step at a time. Josiah turned the metal bar to the right and to the left as he continued to hammer. Finally, after what seemed like a very long time, he was done. He dipped the fork in his tongs into the barrel of water. The water hissed.

Mr. Cooper said, "You did an excellent job, Josiah."

Josiah smiled. "Good thing I had a lot of practice with the nails, or I might not have been ready!"

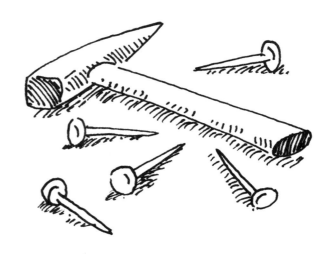

Betsy thought her eyes were playing tricks on her. She couldn't believe it had worked! She rubbed her hands together. "I've read all the genie stories," she said. "I set you free from the jar, so now you have to grant me three wishes."

"One wish," said the genie. "I've only been stuck in the jar for a few months. That's hardly enough time for me to want to be set free. You get one wish and that's it."

Betsy folded her arms and tapped her foot three times. This did not seem fair to her. Why was she getting short-changed? She was about to argue when the genie said, "I wouldn't mind going back in the jar and saving the wish for someone else. The weather out here is a bit chilly today anyway."

"I want my wish!" Betsy exclaimed.

The genie paced around Betsy. "Many people wish they had not made a wish. They end up with less, not more. Think carefully. Once a wish is wished, it can't be undone."

Betsy tapped her toes three more times. She thought, *The two things I like best are the way my shoes go clickety-clack when I tap my toes and the taste of chocolate. I can tap my toes whenever I want, but I can't eat chocolate whenever I want.*

Betsy smiled. "I want to be able to turn things into chocolate."

The genie yawned. "I've granted that wish at least a dozen times. Say the word chocolate and tap your toes three times, for your wish is set. If it's chocolate you want, it's chocolate you'll get."

The genie snapped his fingers and disappeared. Betsy hurried into the kitchen and grabbed a handful of radishes. "Chocolate," she whispered. Clickety-clack, clickety-clack, clickety-clack. Poof! The radishes turned into balls of chocolate. Betsy popped one in her mouth. "Mmm, absolutely delicious!"

Betsy hurried into her room to feed her pet goldfish, Chocolate Drop. She sprinkled the food on top of the water and waited for her fish to eat. Chocolate Drop kept swimming. Betsy grew tired of waiting. "It's time for dinner, Chocolate Drop," she said, tapping her toes impatiently. Poof! Her goldfish became a chocolate fish.

"Poor Chocolate Drop!" Betsy cried. She ran to the park to talk to her friend, Izzy. *Izzy will know how to fix this,* Betsy thought.

When she reached the park, Izzy said, "Let's get some ice cream and then you can tell me what happened. What kind do you want?"

"Chocolate," Betsy answered. Clickety-clack, clickety-clack. Betsy grabbed her foot before the third tap. Could her wish turn her best friend into chocolate too? "Oh dear," said Betsy. "I will have to give up my clickety-clack shoes and never ask for chocolate again."

The Leopard's Spots

Long ago, leopards, zebras, and giraffes roamed the desert. The zebra was easy to spot with his bold black-and-white coat. The giraffe was easy to find too. His long neck and spotted coat were easy to see against the sand. The leopard had a plain coat the color of the golden desert.

The leopard saw his coat as a great fortune. It helped him blend into the desert. His favorite meals were zebras and giraffes. They could move like lightning if they saw an enemy. The leopard might go hungry if he had to race for his dinner. With his golden coat, the leopard could pounce on his dinner without being spotted.

One day, the leopard saw some zebras. They were resting at the edge of the jungle. He tried to creep up beside them. The leopard stood out against the green of the jungle. One zebra spotted him and dashed into the jungle. The others followed at the heels of the first. The leopard followed them. The zebras hid among the different colored plants. The leopard looked and looked for the zebras. Whenever he got close, the zebras spotted the leopard. Then they quickly ran deeper into the jungle. This went on for hours. At last, the hungry leopard gave up.

Soon, all the animals knew what had happened to the leopard. The zebras and giraffes began spending most of their time in the jungle. They felt safe there. The golden leopard grew very hungry. He could not catch his favorite meals. He began to worry he might never eat again.

One day, the leopard was resting under a tree. He spotted some birds eating from a bush. The leopard was so hungry that even the tiny birds seemed worth the chase. He leapt to his feet and ran toward the birds. The birds had fine hearing. When a twig snapped, they sprang from the bush. In their hurry, the birds dropped the blackberries from their beaks.

The golden leopard watched the birds disappear into the sky. Then he looked at the blackberries that had splattered on a nearby log. The leopard smiled. Then he rolled around on the blackberry bush. The blackberries burst against his golden coat. The leopard loved his new spotted coat. He knew the spots would make it easier for others to see him in the desert. The leopard also knew his spots would make it harder for others to spot him in the jungle. Now the hunt would be fair to all.

Cass winds the key on the bottom of the wooden box and places the box on the dresser. A tiny ballerina twirls as music plays. She closes the lid when she hears her brother coming.

Dan flops onto the bed. "I can't believe we never stayed here before. This house reminds me of the haunted houses you see in movies."

Dan and Cass go downstairs for dinner. They see Gran scoop her black cat off the table. "Midnight, you are always getting into trouble."

At bedtime, Cass lifts the lid on the music box again. The ballerina twirls until the music stops. Cass closes the box and winds the key again. When Gran knocks on the door and opens it, Midnight scoots in past Gran's feet. "Midnight likes to stay in here at night, but tonight this is your room. I will take the cat with me."

"Let her stay," Cass says. "We can leave the door cracked, so she can get out if she wants to escape."

Gran tucks Cass into bed and leaves. Midnight leaps onto the bed and curls up by Cass's feet. Later, Cass awakens to the sound of music. The room is as black as coal. Cass hears a snap and realizes the music had been coming from the box on the dresser.

The next morning Cass tells Gran and Dan what happened. Gran says, "Many of my things are so old they don't work properly. There is probably a broken spring in the box that made the music start playing again."

"Or maybe the house really is haunted, and it was a ghost," Dan whispered.

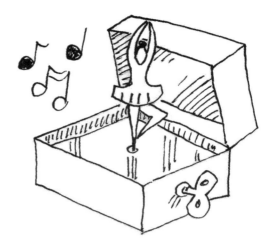

A chill shimmies up Cass's spine. She doesn't believe in ghosts, but a broken spring wouldn't make the box open and close on its own.

The next night, Cass asks Gran for a flashlight to bring to bed with her. When Gran tucks her in, Cass glances nervously at the dresser. "Maybe I should stay in a different room tonight."

Gran kisses Cass's forehead. "I learned long ago that when I faced my fears, the thing I was most afraid of turned out to not be that scary."

When Gran leaves, Cass says to Midnight, "I'm counting on you to protect me tonight."

Once again, Cass awakens to the sound of music. She grabs the flashlight from under her pillow and shines the light on the dresser. Midnight is by the box batting at the ballerina with his paw. The lid slams shut, and Midnight springs off the dresser and back onto the bed.

Cass laughs. "So you are my ghost! It looks like Gran was right!"

Mama admires the blue hat in the mirror and then removes it to read the price tag. "The cost matches the beauty, so it is much too expensive for me." She gently runs her finger along the brim and returns the hat to the rack.

As they exit the store, Mama asks, "Are you going to buy another puzzle book with your spending money?"

"Not this week, Mama," says James. "I'm going to save my money for something bigger."

The next day, Mrs. Potter picks James up from school. James asks his babysitter, "Can we please go to Reynolds' Department Store? Mama took me there yesterday. I want to investigate something."

Mrs. Potter and James ride the bus downtown. James leads Mrs. Potter to the women's hats in the department store. The blue hat is waiting patiently on the shelf. James looks at the price tag and frowns. The sales clerk greets them. "May I help you?"

James digs into his pocket and pulls out a few dollars. "Mama's birthday is in one month. I want to buy her this hat. Can you put it aside until I have

enough money to pay for it? I'll come every week to give you some money."

The sales clerk smiles. "I will take good care of the hat for you."

On the way home, Mrs. Potter says, "That's a great deal of money for a young man to save."

The next day after school, James knocks on his neighbor's front door. "Mr. Rockland, do you have any chores I could do for you?" He tells Mr. Rockland about the hat.

"This porch needs a good sweeping. How are you with a broom?"

"This porch will be as clean as a hospital operating room when I'm finished," James says.

Every day after school, James approaches a neighbor for a job. When he gets home, James deposits his pay in a jar in his dresser drawer.

Every week, Mrs. Potter and James ride the bus downtown to the department store. Soon there is only one week before Mama's birthday. James knows there are not enough chores left undone in the neighborhood to earn the rest of the money he needs.

When he gets home, he opens his baseball card collection. He takes out his favorite card—Johnny "The Rocket" Smith. Billy Reynolds has wanted this card forever.

The next week James returns to the store. The sales clerk wraps the hat and ties a bow on the box. Once home, James stares at the empty space in his card collection. Then he pictures Mama in her hat and smiles.

Sunlight

Wraps me

In golden beams

And warms my spirit.

The old path beckons me

Inviting me up the familiar hill.

The daisies greet me as I pass by.

I try not to disturb my generous hosts.

Boulders act as the guards along the path.

Only a few steps separate me from the castle above.

Finally, I climb into its branches and sit upon the throne.

For at this moment, the kingdom and its beauty are also mine.

The huge circle of flowers surrounding the tree trunk reminds Jake of the quilt on his mother's bed. The baseball is snuggled between rows of pink and yellow flowers about half-way between the grass and the tree. A sign pokes up every few feet along the edge warning people to stay out of the flowers.

"Maybe if you hold me by my belt, I can stretch far enough over the flowers to get the ball," Jake says.

Raj shakes his head. "You'll never be able to reach the ball. Besides, what if I dropped you? You'd leave a Jake-shaped space in the flower bed. Mr. Martinez would know for certain we were the ones trampling his garden."

"Then we need to knock on his door and tell him what happened," Jake says.

"No way!" says Raj. "I heard Mr. Martinez used to be a pirate, and he protects those flowers like he used to protect the diamonds he came across."

Jake laughs. "We don't have pirates around here."

Raj looks nervously at the Martinez house. He lowers his voice. "Have you ever noticed his pool around back? My brother says it's 40 feet deep at the far end. The diving board becomes a plank whenever someone makes Mr. Martinez mad. I'm not a strong enough swimmer to walk the plank and live to talk about it."

Jake eyes his ball again. "That's my brand-new baseball. You can wait here, but I'm going to talk to Mr. Martinez."

Raj watches Jake ring the doorbell on the Martinez house. He strains to hear what his friend says to the owner. Then he sees them walk around the back toward the pool. *Oh no*, Raj thinks, *I have to do something to save my friend*. Two minutes later, Jake and Mr. Martinez come back around front. Mr. Martinez is carrying a long pole with a net on the end of it.

"This is my friend, Raj," Jake says.

Mr. Martinez nods and then reaches over the flowers with the net and scoops up the ball. He hands the ball to Jake. "Thank you, Mr. Martinez. I apologize for bothering you, and I hope the ball didn't hurt your flowers. Raj and I are on the school baseball team. It's the first year for both of us, and we were playing catch to try to get better. We won't practice here anymore."

"Nonsense," says Mr. Martinez. "Practice is the only way to get better. The stories about me being a pirate are true, you know. About 30 years ago, I was the starting pitcher for the Pasadena Pirates. I'd love to practice with you boys. I can share a few winning tips."

"Thanks!" the boys say. Raj grins sheepishly at Jake.

The Case of the Missing Snowshoe Hares

The backyard is covered in a sparkling, white blanket. The fresh snow frosts the tree branches and bushes. "It's beautiful," Tracy says, "but I'm disappointed, Grandma. Last summer when I came to visit, the mother hares had babies. The little ones were hopping around. I expected to see the hares again, but now there are none. Did they move away when they got bigger?"

Grandma shakes her head. "No, they are hidden by the snow."

Tracy smiles. "Then I'm going to sit here until I see one."

When bedtime comes, Tracy asks, "Are you sure they are still out there, Grandma? I sat here for two hours and didn't see a single one of those brown hoppers."

"Oh dear," Grandma says. "If you don't know what you're looking for, you'll never find it. Remember, the hares have their winter coats on this time of year."

The next afternoon, Grandpa asks, "Tracy, do you want to go out to the barn with me? The horses will be looking for their dinner soon."

Tracy puts on her warm coat, hat, and mittens. She pulls on her boots and walks alongside Grandpa in the snow. Once inside the barn, they fill the feed bags and get fresh water for the horses. Before they leave, Grandpa pauses by an old brown horse blanket. "Grandma says you've been searching for the hares. I knew this old blanket would be useful again someday. Let's use it to find the hares."

Grandpa and Tracy leave the barn and walk toward the back of the yard. Grandpa asks, "Do you see our footprints in the snow? If anyone looks behind the house they will know we were here. The hares leave their footprints behind too. Let's see if we can find some."

They walk a little farther and Grandpa points at footprints. "We can track where in the yard the hares visited. There are many prints by that bush, so we know they've been there."

Grandpa drapes the blanket over the bush and the two go inside. After dinner, Grandma and Grandpa sit with Tracy by the window. The full moon helps them see the brown blanket on the shrub. Then Tracy sees three white hares hopping in front of the blanket.

"Look! The brown hares didn't come back, but some white ones are out there."

"Those are the same hares," Grandma says. "Do you remember me telling you they had their winter coats on? The hares are brown in the summer and white in the winter."

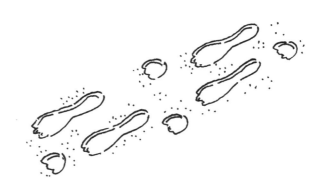

The four oranges on the table were a greater opponent than Lev had ever faced across a chess board. He could handle two easily. Lev felt confident he could master three too, but four were simply too much to ask of him. "You're asking me to do the impossible. Besides, oranges are for eating—not tossing," Lev said.

"Hardly impossible," Andy said. "If I can do it, you can do it. We struck a deal: I learn something you're good at, and you learn something I'm good at. If I can shoulder losing countless chess games to you, you can deal with the disappointment of dropping a few oranges. Juggling is fun if you open your mind to it. The oranges don't bounce around as much as small rubber balls do when you drop them. The oranges are also easier to grip than smooth rubber balls."

Lev picked up two of the small oranges and tossed them one by one from hand to hand. He liked the way his palms felt when the weight of the oranges landed in the centers of them. The bumpy skin did make them easier to grasp. He picked up a third orange and tossed it into the air. Keeping three oranges moving between two hands was much more difficult. Thud! Thud! Thud! When one fell, the others followed. "I can't do this," Lev moans.

Andy sighed. "Think about the train story you are always reading to your little brother. Stop saying, 'I can't' and start saying, 'I can.' I have to go to the library to check out a new book on chess. I'll beat you soon!"

Lev stared at the oranges after Andy left. He picked up three and tried again. "I think I can; I think I can; I think I can," he chanted.

The oranges sailed in an arc through the air, passing from hand to hand. Lev's heart raced until the oranges escaped his grip once more. Lev took a deep breath, picked up the oranges, and started again. "I think I can; I think I can; I think I can," he chanted.

For several days, Lev practiced with three oranges. Then he invited Andy over to see the progress he had made. The oranges sailed effortlessly through the air as Lev demonstrated what he had mastered.

As Lev juggled, he chanted to the rhythm of the dance of the oranges. "I know I can; I know I can; I know I can."

"Excellent!" cheered Andy. "I think you might be able to juggle four oranges soon. Now where is your chess board? Prepare yourself to hear the word checkmate!"

The Incredible Edible Town

A police officer watches as a woman pulls carrots from the police station garden patch. The woman drops the carrots in her basket and hurries off. A few minutes later, a man enters the garden. He digs up a few potatoes, drops them in a bag, and leaves. At this rate, the garden will be empty before long. What does the officer do about this? He smiles.

The police station garden is a public garden. People can take the vegetables, and they don't have to pay. There are at least 70 free gardens in this small town in England. The name of the town is Todmorden, but the people who live there call it Tod. Tod is earning a new name now—The Incredible Edible Town.

Along with the police station, there are gardens near the health center, the train station, and the canal path. There are also gardens on the college lawns, in the town center, and along parking lots. Herbs grow in some beds. Fruits and vegetables grow in others. There are also fruit trees and berry bushes to pick from.

The gardens work on an honor system. It doesn't matter who took the last radish or strawberry. No one keeps track. People take what they or their families will eat and leave the rest. When the garden is bare, a new crop is planted.

The town wasn't always like this. The change started with a small group of women who wanted to make a positive change. They decided to plant vegetable gardens around town. One of the women planted a garden in her front yard. When the vegetables were ready to pick, she put up a sign that told people to take whatever they needed. At first, no one came into her garden. But slowly, that changed. People picked what they needed and left the rest for other people.

The idea began to grow. The group planted vegetables in the center of town. The people in town loved the idea. So the group planted more beds, trees, and bushes around town. Many restaurants and schools in Tod serve only veggies and fruit grown locally.

Gardens take time and money. Many people in town donate money or materials to the project. Groups and companies chip in too. Other people give their time to plant and care for the gardens. Some teach free gardening classes or free cooking classes. There are even free classes in jam and jelly making. The people in town are learning how to grow and prepare their own food.

The free garden project in Tod is a success. The idea is now spreading to other towns and even other countries, such as Spain and New Zealand.

What can we learn from sharks? A lot, say **biomimicry** experts. Biomimicry scientists study nature. Then they try to **imitate**, or copy, it to solve problems or make something better. Studying sharks is helping people solve many problems. People are copying the **texture** of sharkskin and using it to create new things.

Sharkskin is covered in tiny, grooved, V-shaped scales. As the shark swims, water flows through each groove. As a result, the shark can swim faster. The scales help the shark in another way too. There are lots of bacteria and **algae**, a tiny form of life, in the ocean. These things stick to most kinds of fish and whales. The texture of sharkskin keeps bacteria and algae from sticking to the shark.

Experts took a close look at sharkskin. Then they copied the texture in different materials. One of those materials is an imitation sharkskin fabric or cloth. They used the cloth to make swimsuits. Some swimmers wore the imitation sharkskin swimsuits in the Olympics. The swimmers wearing the special suits won more races than those who wore other kinds of suits. These types of suits are now banned.

People have also made paint that imitates sharkskin. They use the paint on many things. Painting the blades of windmills with the sharkskin-like paint helps the blades spin faster. The experts are also testing the paint on the outside of airplanes. The air will flow through the grooves like the water does on a shark's skin. This will help the plane go faster and save fuel.

Experts also tested the paint on the **hulls**, or bottoms, of ships. The ships went faster and used less fuel, but the paint did something more for the ships. It kept bacteria and algae from sticking to the ship. Cleaning boat hulls is hard work, so the paint saved the owners both work and money.

The cleaner ship hulls gave the experts another idea. If the sharkskin texture can keep bacteria off a ship, maybe it would work in hospitals. Some kinds of bacteria make people sick. Hospitals use medicines and chemicals to fight these germs. But this does not work for all kinds of bacteria. The experts made another new material called **biofilm**. It is rough, like sharkskin. In the test, the film helped keep germs off the surfaces it covered, like counters.

Scientists are still finding new ways to use what they have learned from sharks. Who knows what problems they will solve tomorrow?

In 1871, a terrible fire swept through the city of Chicago. People often blame the Great Chicago Fire on a cow. But what really caused the fire?

Chicago was once a small city. The growth of the railroads brought more people to the city. As the population grew, so did the need for housing and jobs. Buildings went up at a fast rate. But the wooden buildings were often poorly made. People called Chicago "the wooden city." They even used wood boards for streets and sidewalks.

Almost no rain fell for three months during the summer of 1871. By October, the sun had dried out all the wood. Yards and parks were covered in brown, dead grass. People were filling their sheds with dry hay for their animals to prepare for winter.

The city's firefighters had battled a fire every day during October. By the day the Great Fire broke out, the men were exhausted. Their equipment was also not in good condition.

The fire began in the evening of October 8, 1871. The fire started in the barn behind Patrick and Catherine O'Leary's house. The wind carried the flames to the east and to the north. More and more homes and businesses caught fire. The fire burned for two days, destroying everything in its path. Finally, on the morning of October 10, it began to rain. The fire finally died.

The entire center of Chicago was gone. Homes, businesses, and churches were ruined. About 73 miles of streets had burned. At least 100,000 people had no homes, and 300 people had died.

But the people of Chicago did not let the fire bring them down. The next day, William D. Kerfoot reopened his real estate business in an old shed. He hung a sign by his door that read, "All gone but WIFE, CHILDREN, and ENERGY." Kerfoot was ready to get back to work.

Many people felt it was time to start over. The next month, Chicago elected a new mayor. He promised to make stricter building and fire laws to help make the city safer. The people began to rebuild, including some of the world's first skyscrapers. The new buildings were safer. In years to come, many more people came to Chicago.

The day after the fire, a newspaper ran a story about how the fire started. It claimed one of the O'Leary's cows had knocked over a lantern and set the hay on fire. Later, the reporters said they had made the story up. Yet, some people still blame a cow for the Great Chicago Fire.

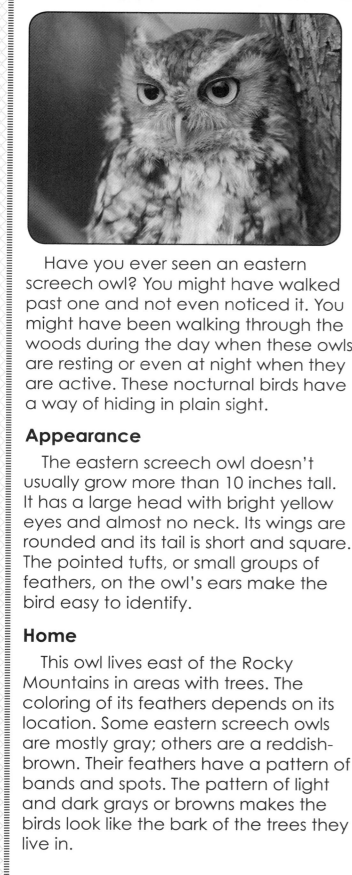

Have you ever seen an eastern screech owl? You might have walked past one and not even noticed it. You might have been walking through the woods during the day when these owls are resting or even at night when they are active. These nocturnal birds have a way of hiding in plain sight.

Appearance

The eastern screech owl doesn't usually grow more than 10 inches tall. It has a large head with bright yellow eyes and almost no neck. Its wings are rounded and its tail is short and square. The pointed tufts, or small groups of feathers, on the owl's ears make the bird easy to identify.

Home

This owl lives east of the Rocky Mountains in areas with trees. The coloring of its feathers depends on its location. Some eastern screech owls are mostly gray; others are a reddish-brown. Their feathers have a pattern of bands and spots. The pattern of light and dark grays or browns makes the birds look like the bark of the trees they live in.

Spotting the Screech Owl

It can be harder to spot an eastern screech owl in the day than at night. The owl makes its home in a small opening in a tree. During the day, it rests there, staying perfectly still with its eyes closed. In this way, it makes itself blend in with the tree trunk. You could walk by the tree and not know the bird is there. At night, the bird is more active. It leaves its nest to hunt for food and makes a series of trilling or whinnying sounds. These sounds let you know a screech owl is near. Still, the bird will find a tree to blend in with if people or other dangers come near. Hiding is a way the bird protects itself.

So if you are on the lookout for an eastern screech owl, follow these simple steps: Be quiet and listen for the trill. Then study the bark of the trees carefully. Don't get too close, though. Owls are wild animals, and they might attack if they feel threatened.

Watch Out!

Even though eastern screech owls usually hide from people, they will protect their nests. The owls line the opening in the tree with soft nesting materials. They lay their eggs there. If a person is coming too close to the nest, the owl will swoop down and thwack the person on the head. It is the bird's way of saying, "Stay away from my nest!"

Bike helmets can save lives, but only if people wear them. In Sweden, many people bike to school, work, and shops. About 80 percent of the people there ride their bikes every day. Yet, only about 20 percent of adult riders wear a bike helmet. Anna Haupt and Terese Alstin rode bikes every day in Sweden. They wanted to come up with a way to make bike riding safer.

Understanding the Problem

Terese and Anna looked into the problem in Sweden. They didn't like what they learned. More than two dozen people die in bicycle accidents every year. A few hundred more people have head injuries. Why weren't more people wearing helmets?

Anna and Terese talked to many people. They learned adults didn't wear helmets because of the way the helmets looked and felt on their heads. Adults also didn't like the way their hair looked when they took the helmets off. They didn't want to go to work with "helmet head."

Finding a Solution

In 2005, the women set out to find a way to make a helmet people would want to wear. But it also had to be safe. They looked closely at bicycle accidents. The women watched how the riders moved during different kinds of falls. Finally, they came up with an idea for an invisible bike helmet. They called it a Hövding. This invisible bike helmet is really an airbag for your head. It only opens and covers your head in an accident.

The Hövding looks like a scarf, and it comes in lots of colors and prints. A rider puts it around her neck and zips it up. Then she pushes a button to turn it on. The airbag is made of nylon, which is a tough material. It won't rip or break when it hits the ground. Each scarf also has a tiny gas tube and a rechargeable battery. The battery starts the tube, which fills the scarf with helium gas in the event of an accident. This only takes one-tenth of a second.

The women set up many test accidents to see if the scarves would work. They used all they learned to make the Hövding ready for sale. The new bike helmet went on sale in Sweden in 2012.

There are a couple of problems with the Hövding, however. One problem is that after the Hövding inflates in an accident, it cannot be used again. And the cost to buy a new one is very expensive.

Still, Anna and Terese hope the Hövding will bring about a big change in Sweden and throughout the world. They hope more and more riders will choose to be safe on their bikes.

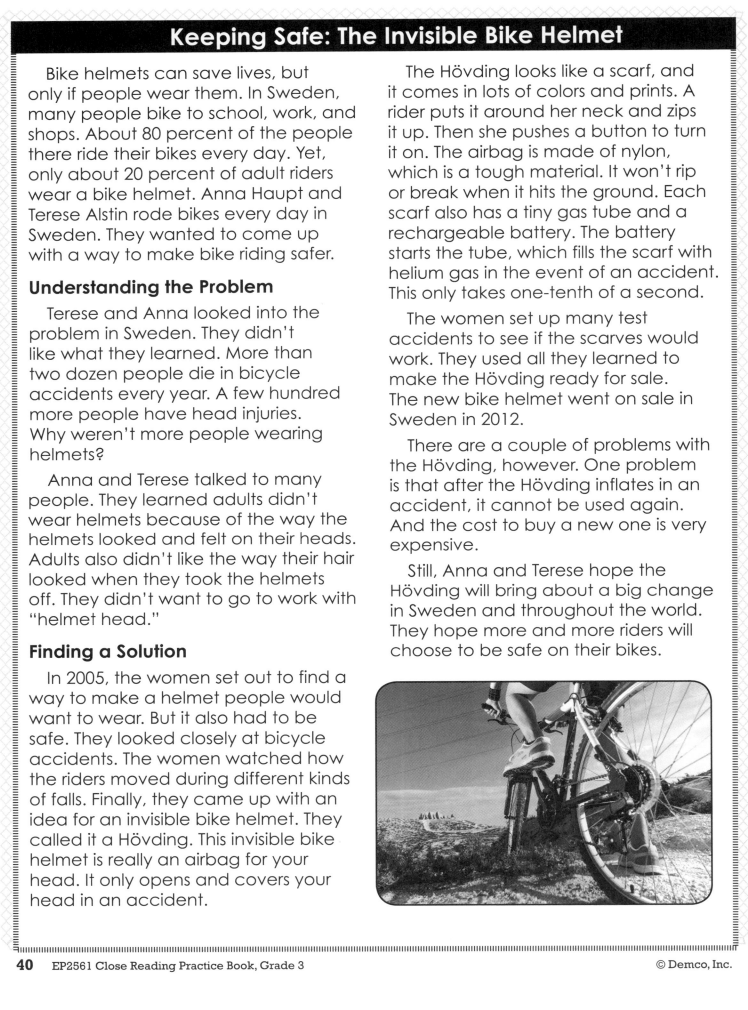

Dr. Jenner's Dangerous Experiment

It was the late 1700s. People knew little about how the body fought disease. Smallpox was spreading. Just the word "smallpox" struck fear in people's hearts.

Smallpox was a disease that spread quickly among people. At one time, one out of every three to four people who got smallpox died from it. The disease caused high fevers and covered people's faces and bodies with a rash of liquid-filled sores. The sores left scabs when they dried up. When the scabs fell off, they left scars.

Edward Jenner was a doctor in England. At this time, doctors had only one way to try to stop or limit the spread of smallpox. They took liquid from the sores of a person with a mild case of smallpox. A doctor then put the liquid into a healthy person by scratching the person's arm and rubbing it in. If the person got a mild case of smallpox and recovered, that person would not get it again. Sometimes this worked. However, people often died from this.

In 1788, smallpox hit the small town where Dr. Jenner lived. There were many cattle farms there. Dr. Jenner noticed the cow-farm workers weren't dying from the disease. He knew many farm workers had already had cowpox. Cows get cowpox on their skin. It causes sores, too, but it is much milder than smallpox. Cowpox can spread from cows to the people who milk them. Dr. Jenner thought that farm workers who had already had cowpox were better able to fight off smallpox.

A milkmaid named Sarah Nelmes visited Dr. Jenner on May 1, 1796. She

had cowpox sores on her hands. Dr. Jenner took some of the liquid from the sores.

Dr. Jenner talked to a farmer in the area. He explained the connection he saw between cowpox and smallpox. He asked the farmer for permission to experiment on the farmer's eight-year-old son. The farmer agreed. He hoped the experiment would prevent his son from getting smallpox. On May 14, Dr. Jenner made two small cuts in the arm of James Phipps. He rubbed the cowpox liquid into the cuts. The boy became ill with cowpox, but soon he was better.

Then, in July, Dr. Jenner repeated his actions. However, this time he used smallpox liquid. If Dr. Jenner's idea was correct, it could save millions of lives. If he was wrong, a child could die. But the boy did not become ill. This meant that Dr. Jenner's idea worked. The cowpox stopped James from getting smallpox.

At first, many people didn't believe in Dr. Jenner's smallpox vaccine. Slowly, people changed their minds. By 1800, the vaccine had reached many other countries. Finally, in 1980, the World Health Assembly said "the world and its peoples" were free from smallpox.

The Venus Flytrap

You know that some bugs eat plants, but did you know that some plants eat bugs? In the wild, **carnivorous**, or meat-eating, plants grow mainly in areas where the soil cannot provide all of the **nutrients** the plants need to survive. Instead, the plants get those nutrients from eating bugs. Some even eat small rodents, like mice!

The Venus flytrap is the most well-known meat-eating plant. Venus flytraps eat many different kinds of bugs. As a matter of fact, they eat more spiders, ants, beetles, and grasshoppers than flies.

The Venus flytrap is a flowering plant that blooms year after year. The plant's flowers grow on top of a shoot, above the leaves. A fully grown plant usually has seven leaves. Each leaf has two **lobes** that open wide. There is a row of short **bristles** around the outer rim of each lobe. Inside the lobes, several tiny hairs grow. These stiff hairs are called **triggers**.

Sweet **nectar** oozes across each leaf lobe. The scent of the nectar draws bugs to the plants. When the bug goes to eat the tasty nectar, it walks along the surface of the leaf. If it touches a trigger hair, the bug sets off the trapping process. If the bug moves a trigger again within 20 seconds, the lobes snap shut.

The bug is trapped inside. It takes less than a second for the trap to close. The leaf doesn't close all the way at first. The bristles look like prison bars at this point. Small bugs, which wouldn't provide much food for the plant, now have a few seconds to escape through the bars. The trap then seals completely, and the bristles lock together. The bug is squeezed between the lobes.

Glands inside the trap make juices that help the plant digest the bug. It takes five to 10 days for the plant to digest the bug. It only eats the soft insides of the bug and leaves the hard shell. When the plant is finished eating, the lobes open wide again. Rain or wind carries away the leftover parts of the bug.

The number of Venus flytraps growing in the wild is shrinking. The plants grow in the cleared floors of forests. One thing that clears the forest floor is natural fires caused by things like lightning. Today, the fires often are a danger to people living nearby, so they are not allowed to burn freely. This leaves less open ground. Another problem is people's interest in the plants. Many of the wild plants are dug up and potted. Their seeds are used to grow more plants in greenhouses.

More than 750 types of meat-eating plants have been discovered.

Wilson Bentley loved science. He loved art too. He found a way to bring them together. Wilson was born on February 9, 1865. His family lived in snowy Vermont. Wilson built a career with snowflakes. This earned him the nickname "Snowflake" Bentley.

Wilson's mother taught him at home. As a child, he loved learning about rain and snow. Wilson helped his father on the farm too. This let him be outside where he could watch the bugs and birds.

Wilson's mother gave him a special gift for his 15th birthday. It was a microscope. Wilson used his gift to look at snowflakes. He was amazed by what he saw. Each flake was complex and unique. Wilson tried to draw the snowflakes, but he never had enough time to finish. The snowflake melted too fast. How could he share the beauty of snowflakes with others? Wilson knew a camera was the answer to his problem. But in the late 1800s, cameras were very costly.

Wilson finally got a camera when he was 17. Then the hard work began. Wilson had an idea. He attached his microscope to his camera. He stood out in the cold for hours at a time and waited for snow to fall. When it did, he caught a snowflake on a feather and moved it to the microscope. Then he took a picture of it.

Wilson spent two years trying to get a good picture of a snowflake. Finally, it worked. Wilson took the first photograph of a snowflake when he was 19 years old. It was the first of many. During his life, Wilson took 5,000 snowflake pictures.

At first, people thought Wilson's photos were some kind of trick. They didn't believe what he did was possible. But this changed over time. He published many photographs and articles in science journals. In 1931, a book of his snowflake images was published.

Wilson's photos also helped him make an important scientific discovery. He learned that no two snowflakes are alike.

Wilson was interested in other types of weather as well. In fact, he recorded the weather every day for 47 years. He filled nine notebooks with his observations. He also studied and wrote about frost, dew, and rain. Sadly, in 1931, Wilson died from pneumonia after walking home during a blizzard.

Today, Wilson "Snowflake" Bentley is thought of as a pioneer in the fields of weather and photography.

Photomicrography

Wilson Bentley was a pioneer in **photomicrography**. This is the art of photographing very small objects.

In August of 1587, 118 people arrived on North Carolina's Roanoke Island. Three years later, they were gone. They left behind two clues. One was the word "Croatoan." It was carved in the gatepost of the colony's fort. It was the name of a nearby island. The second clue was only three letters long. Someone had scratched "Cro" into a tree. What happened to the people?

The colonists were the third group England sent to the island. Sir Walter Raleigh sent the first group in 1584. Their job was to scout the area. The men made maps and returned to England.

The next year, Raleigh sent 100 men to the island. They were soldiers, miners, and scientists. Ralph Lowe led the group. The men arrived after the planting season ended. They quickly ran out of supplies. There were also problems between the soldiers and a Native American tribe. The tribe didn't like the way Lowe's men treated them or the land and its resources. Fighting broke out. Lowe's men left the island.

In 1587, Raleigh sent another group. This time, there were men, women, and children. Their purpose was to settle a colony. They lived in a fort. It was a small village with a tall fence around it.

Life was difficult for the people. John White, the leader of the colony, returned to England to get more supplies for the people. When he got to England, the country was at war with Spain. There were no ships to spare. White finally returned to Roanoke Island with new supplies three years later. The fort was empty. White's family and friends were all gone.

Where did the people go? There are many theories. One is that the people simply gave up. They tried to get back to England on their own, but they got lost at sea. A second idea is that the people were captured or killed by Spanish explorers. Spain had colonies in Florida. Was it trying to get more land?

A third idea is that the people got sick and died. There likely was bacteria on the island the people hadn't been around before. Their bodies couldn't fight the germs. Another idea says the Native American tribe Lowe fought with was still angry and attacked the fort. The fifth idea builds on the others. The people faced some great danger. They broke into smaller groups and went in different directions. They were taken in by friendly Native Americans.

Researchers recently studied again an old map of the island, made by John White. The map has patches on it, and they wanted to see what was under the patches. The researchers found a tiny red and blue symbol. The symbol might mark an emergency meeting spot or a secret fort. New technology helps scientists see things their unaided eyes can't see. With the help of this technology, the scientists looked under the ground marked on the map. They think they see wooden structures and fence buried there. They will have to dig. Could this finding help solve the mystery of the Lost Colony?

A Race Against Time

In 1924, the people of Nome were used to being on their own. No railroad lines reached this small town in western Alaska. There weren't any big roads, either. This winter was especially hard. The weather had practically cut the small town off from the world. Sea ice made it too dangerous for ships to visit the area. The weather also stopped planes from landing there. It looked like the town was on its own. Then disaster struck.

Curtis Welch was the only doctor in town. In December, he saw several children with sore throats. Dr. Welch treated them, but they became sicker. Two of the children died in January 1925. Dr. Welch knew things were going to get worse. This was because the children didn't just have a sore throat. They had diphtheria.

Diphtheria causes the throat and neck to swell. This makes it hard to breathe. The disease spreads quickly through coughing and sneezing. Dr. Welch put the sick children in quarantine. They were kept away from healthy people. But Dr. Welch knew it was too late. The disease had already had a chance to spread.

There was only one way to treat the illness and stop it from spreading. The doctor needed antitoxin serum. The doctor's supply was six years old. He feared that this was too old. Could it hurt people instead of help them? The town needed fresh serum, and they needed it fast. Dr. Curtis asked U.S. leaders for help. There was only one way to get the medicine to Nome.

The serum was sent by train to the nearest station, which was far from Nome. Dog sleds would carry it from the train station to Nome. They would travel along the Iditarod Trail through dangerous mountain ranges. Meanwhile, the governor rounded up 20 of Alaska's best mail mushers. A musher is someone who drives a dog sled.

The trip usually took 15 to 20 days. But that was too long. The mushers would work in relay fashion. This way, the medicine would be moving around the clock. The first musher and his team started out at 9 p.m. on January 27. When he reached the next musher, the medicine was moved into the new sled. Then the second musher set off. The mushers traveled through blizzards and temperatures that dipped down to 50 degrees below zero. Some of the mushers got frostbite, and some of the dogs didn't survive the trip. But at 5:30 a.m. on February 2, the serum arrived in Nome. The mushers had made the trip in five days and seven hours. Today, this journey is known as the Great Race of Mercy.

Two weeks after the serum arrived, the quarantine was over. Dr. Welch believed hundreds of lives were saved by the heroic actions of the mushers.

More than 150 sled dogs were needed to make the 674-mile trip to Nome.

The Clothesline Code

One black petticoat and three white hankies hung on the clothesline. Two people knew what that meant. To others, it just looked like laundry day.

The clothes belonged to Anna Strong. Anna was a spy. During the American Revolution, a group of colonists, called Patriots, wanted freedom from England. Not everyone in the colonies felt that way. Many, known as Loyalists, stayed true to England and the king. Often neighbors were on opposite sides of the war. At the time, there were no telephones or telegraphs. Spy rings were a way to share information and warn troops about the other side's actions. Anna was a part of the Culper Spy Ring. The ring helped George Washington win the American Revolution.

Anna lived on a farm in Long Island, New York. Anna and her husband, Silah, who was a judge, wanted the colonies to be free from England. One day, British soldiers arrested Silah and put him on a prison ship. Anna gave the soldiers money to set her husband free. Silah could not go back to the farm. Instead, he went to live with his family in Connecticut. Anna stayed so that soldiers would not take the farm.

George Washington asked Benjamin Tallmadge, an army captain, to put together a spy ring. Secret messages would go back and forth through the ring. Robert Townsend was one of the spies. He owned a shop in New York City. He also worked for a newspaper there, writing about big parties and other fun events. British soldiers met and talked at the parties. Robert listened for clues to what the British would do next.

Another spy, Austin Roe, visited Robert's shop. Austin would buy something and also leave written requests for information. After Austin left, Robert would write a message back. He then waited for Austin to come back and hid the secret message in the package with the goods Austin bought. Next, Austin rode his horse back to Long Island. Austin hid the message in a box in a field.

Arthur Woodhull lived near the field. He picked up the note and got it to Caleb Brewster. He took the messages across the water to Connecticut. When Arthur needed to find Caleb, he looked at Anna's clothesline. A black petticoat meant Caleb was somewhere in Long Island. Next, he looked at the hankies. If Anna hung three hankies, Caleb was waiting in the third bay.

After Arthur gave Caleb the note, Caleb rowed over to Connecticut. Tallmadge met him there. He took the message and rode off on horseback. Tallmadge passed the note on to a soldier. Every 15 miles, the note moved on to a new soldier. It stopped when it reached George Washington in upstate New York.

The Culper Spy Ring was one of the most successful spy groups in the war. Anna never got caught. After the war, her husband came back to the farm. They raised their family there.

Do you have ideas for things that could help make people's lives easier or more fun? Does this make you want to be an inventor when you grow up? You can be an inventor now!

New Solutions

There have been kid inventors for hundreds of years. Margaret E. Knight was born in 1838. Many children at that time worked in factories. Margaret worked in a mill that made cloth. One day, she saw a shuttle fly off a machine. A shuttle holds thread on a loom. It hit and hurt one of the workers. Margaret was only 12. She already knew there should be a way to stop this from happening. She invented a safety clip to keep the shuttle in place. She later invented many other things, like the flat-bottomed paper bag.

Accidental Discoveries

Sometimes kids invent things when they aren't even trying to do so. In 1905, Frank Epperson was 11 years old. He lived with his family in San Francisco. One day he went out on the porch of their home. He mixed some soda powder with water. Then Frank got busy and forgot about the flavored water. That night it got very cold outside. Frank went out on the porch in the morning. His soda water was frozen solid. The wooden stick he had used to stir it was still in it. Frank had invented the first Popsicle.

Fun Inventions

George Nissan was a kid inventor too. The year was 1930. George was 16 years old. He got an idea while watching trapeze artists. The artists would drop down from their swings into a safety net. They would bounce a bit when they hit the net. George thought it would be great if they could bounce longer. They could do more flips and tricks after they landed. George started to think about what they could land on other than a net. He went to work in his garage. He stretched a piece of canvas over a metal frame. He called it a "bouncing rig." Later in college, he replaced the canvas with nylon. This material gave more bounce. He changed the name too. The Spanish word *trampolín* means diving board. George added an 'e' to the end and named his bouncing rig a trampoline.

Contests

Today, there are many contests for young inventors. Some ask kids to find new ways to use old products. There are also contests that ask kids to come up with a new product or make something better. Kids are finding new ways to play, cook, work, and travel. So don't wait until you're older to put your ideas in action. You could be the next kid to have a great invention!

The Mysterious Mother Goose

Most of us know the same rhymes. We learned "Little Bo Peep" and "Three Blind Mice" before we went to school. The same is true of "Miss Muffet," "Humpty Dumpty," and "Jack and Jill." Did one person, Mother Goose, write all these rhymes? Who is the mysterious Mother Goose? Is she even real?

The name Mother Goose was in print hundreds of years ago.

- 1650 – A book titled *The History of Muse* by Jean Loret was made. It included the words, "like a Mother Goose story."
- 1697 – Charles Perrault published a book of fairy tales, with the subtitle *Tales of Mother Goose*.
- 1760 – John Newbery published *Mother Goose's Melody*. It was a book of rhymes.

Newbery's book was a hit. Many people copied it without his permission. They sold the copies all over England and in New York and Boston. Some of these books had more rhymes added. Mother Goose became well known, and people wondered about the writer. Who was she? Where was she from?

People started telling stories about who Mother Goose was. In one story, she was a French queen named Queen Bertrada. She lived from about 710 to 783. People called her "Goose-footed Bertha." The word "goose" is the only thing tying the queen to Mother Goose. There is no proof she even liked rhymes.

Another story points to Elizabeth Goose. She lived from 1665 to 1758 in Boston. She and her husband raised 16 children. Elizabeth sang songs and rhymes to her children and grandchildren. Her son-in-law worked in the book business. He put her rhymes in a book and called her Mother Goose.

The story does make Elizabeth sound more like Mother Goose than the queen did. Yet, there are holes in that story too. First, no one can find that Mother Goose book. Second, Elizabeth was born in 1665. That is years after the name Mother Goose was used in other books.

So who is the real Mother Goose? No one is certain. Most likely the rhymes came from many different people—both men and women. Like folktales, the rhymes probably were passed down. A man recites a rhyme to his daughter. The daughter grows up and recites the same rhyme to her son. At some point, people started writing them down. The name itself was probably made up. We might never solve the mystery of Mother Goose. However, we will likely share the rhymes for years to come.

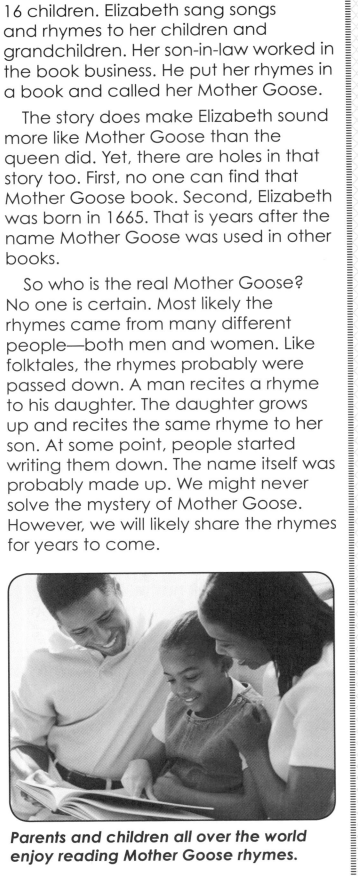

Parents and children all over the world enjoy reading Mother Goose rhymes.